the best of mike oldfield elements

Worldwide Representation: Clive Banks Limited
P.O. Box 2865, London W6 0LT
Folio © 1994 International Music Publications Limited
Southend Road, Woodford Green, Essex IG8 8HN England
Cover Artwork: Bill Smith
Music Transcribed by Barnes Music Engraving Ltd.,
East Sussex TN22 4HA
Printed by Panda Press · Haverhill · Suffolk CB9 8PR

215-2-1118

Apart from *Tubular Bells* which is presented in its entirety, this collection is a snap-shot of Mike's work on the Virgin label. That work spans almost two decades in which studio and musical technology have undergone dramatic developments and the world in general has experienced great political and social change. He has described himself as an "ambassador for instrumental music" though his music bears little relationship to the often tuneless New Age style that has done so much damage to the credibility of the long instrumental format.

Through all of this Mike has continued to create and develop his art, constantly exploring every advance in musical technology and incorporating influences and sounds from around the world. Welcome to the first eighteen years' work of one of Britain's greatest composers and instrumentalists.

Richard Newman and Dave Laing

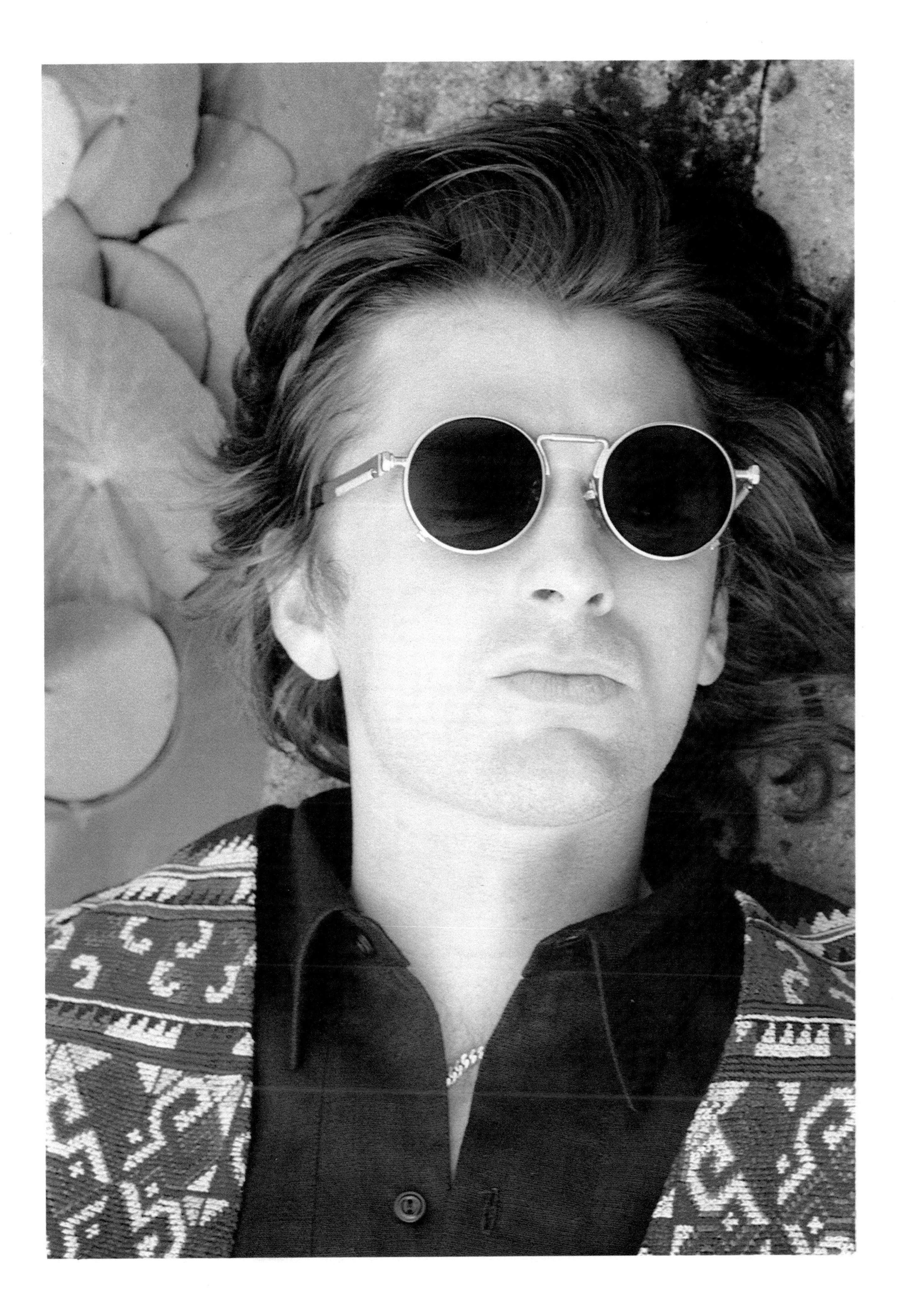

family man

Words and Music by
Mike Oldfield, Mike Frye, Tim Cross,
Richard Fenn, Maggie Reilly and Morris Pert

D♭ E♭ Fm

— me a-lone— I'm a fa-mi-ly man— if you push— me too far,— I just might."

Fm

Guitar Solo on *D.*𝄋 only

D♭ E♭ Fm

3

D♭ E♭ Fm

3

Fm7
Fm
Bb/F
Fm9
Eb/F
Db
Eb
to Coda
2. She wore hurt sur - prise as she re - checked her make - up to pro - tect her - self. She showed less than pride she made it to - tal - ly clear that she was his for a price.
3. She gave him her look it would have worked on an - y oth - er man in sight. He could not mis - take she want - ed to go back with him and spend this night. But he said, "Leave me a - lone I'm a fa - mi - ly man and my bark is much worse then my bite. Please just leave
4. She turned tossed her head and then she start - ed to make her fi - nal ex - it line. She showed real dis - dain and start - ed scream - ing a - gain, she could be his for a price.

D♭
E♭
Fm
1st time repeat
2nd time D.𝄋 al Coda
me a - lone I'm a fa - mi - ly man if you push me too far I just might."
CODA
"Leave me a - lone I'm a fa - mi - ly man and my bark is much worse than my bite."
He said, "Leave me a - lone I'm a fa - mi - ly man if you
1.2.3.
4.
push me too far I just might." But he said, push me too far I just might."

moonlight shadow

Words & Music by
Mike Oldfield

E B C♯m A B
Lost in a rid-dle that Sat-ur-day night, far a-way on the oth-er___ side._ He was
All she saw_ was a sil-hou-ette of a gun, far a-way on the oth-er___ side._ He was
stars move slow-ly in a sil-ver-y light, far a-way on the oth-er___ side._ Will you
E B C♯m A
1. B
4fr
caught in the mid-dle of a des-perate fight, and she could-n't find how to push through._ The
shot six times by a man on the run, and she could-n't find how to push
come to talk to me___ this___ night but she could-n't find how to push
2.3. B
E B E B E A B E B
2fr
through. I stay, I pray, see_ you in hea-ven far a-way.
E B E B E A B E B
I stay, I pray, see_ you in hea-ven_ one day.

C♯m
4fr
A
B
E
B
Guitar solo
C♯m
4fr
A
B
E
B
E
B
C♯m
4fr
A
B
E
B
C♯m
4fr
A
B

C♯m
4fr
A
B
E
B
C♯m
4fr
A
B
E
B
E
B
C♯m
4fr
A
B
Caught in the mid-dle of a hun-dred and five.
Guitar
The
E
B
C♯m
4fr
A
B
fade on repeat
night was hea-vy and the air was so live, but she could-n't find how to push through.
Guitar

heaven's open

Words & Music by
Mike Oldfield

C
D
Dsus2
G6/B
Bm
Em
D
This is that morn - ing, it's wait - ing for you,
C
D
Dsus4
G/B
Bm
Em
D/F♯
the face of des - ti - ny stand - ing be - fore you.
G
D/F♯
Em
Csus2
3fr
D5
2fr
This is ze - ro hour, now is for you.
G
D/F♯
Em
Csus2
3fr
D5
2fr
Can you feel that pow-er, in - side of you?

C
D
Dsus4
G/B
Bm
Em
D
This price - less mo - ment, in your pos-ses - sion,
C
D
Dsus4
G/B
Bm
Em
D/F♯
ans - wers to my - ster - ies stand in suc - ces - sion.
G
D/F♯
Em
Csus2
3fr
D5
2fr
This is ze - ro hour and there's no way back.
G
D/F♯
Em
Csus2
3fr
D5
2fr
Can you feel that pow-er? In its arms you're wrapped.

G Csus2 3fr Dsus4 Em7 C Dsus4
All through the night-time, till the sun comes in now
G C D Em C D G
hea - ven's o - pen, just fly right in.
Electric guitar
Em D G D C D Em
C D G D C D G

C
D
Dsus4
G/B
Bm
Em
D
Now you stand in that garden, this is that vision.
C
Dsus4
D
Bm
Em
D/F♯
Out on the world's edge, it's your baptism.
3
G
D/F♯
Em
Csus2
3fr
D5
2fr
This is zero hour and your hands are free.
G
D/F♯
Em
Csus2
3fr
D5
2fr
Can you feel that power? It's ecstasy.

G
Csus2
3fr
Dsus4
Em7
C
Dsus4
All through the night-time, till the sun comes in. Now
G
C
D
Em
C
D
G
Electric guitar
heaven's open, fly right in.
Em
D
G
D
C
D
Em
C
D
G
D
C
D
G

N.C. G N.C. C D N.C. D Em N.C. C N.C. C N.C. C Dsus4 N.C.
Wait - ing the whole night - time, till the sun comes in.
G N.C. C D N.C. D Em N.C. C N.C. C D N.C. D N.C. G N.C.
All through the night - time, let the blue sky in.
G5
3fr
Hea - ven's o - pen, the sun comes in.
Hea - ven's o - pen, let that blue sky in.

G
Csus2
3fr
Dsus4
Em7
C
Dsus4
You know the sun comes in now
G
C
D
Em
C
N.C.
Electric guitar
heav - en's o - pen,
fly right in.
Em
D
G
D
C
D
Em
C
D
G
D
C
D
G

five miles out

Words & Music by
Mike Oldfield

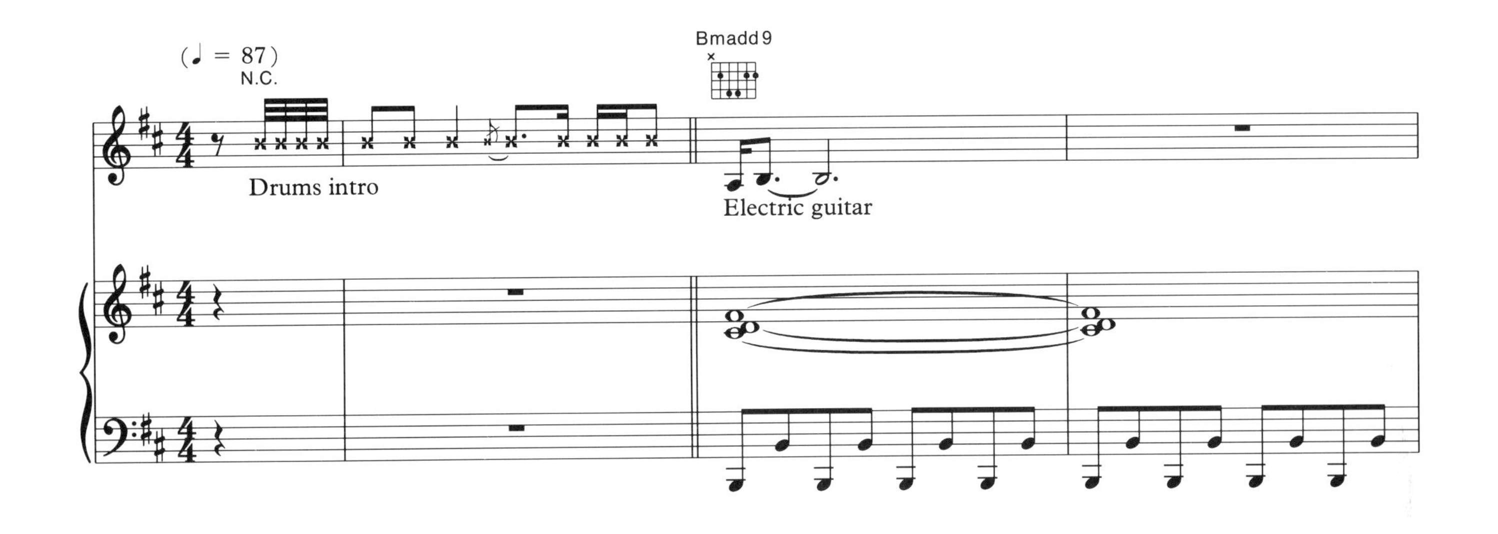

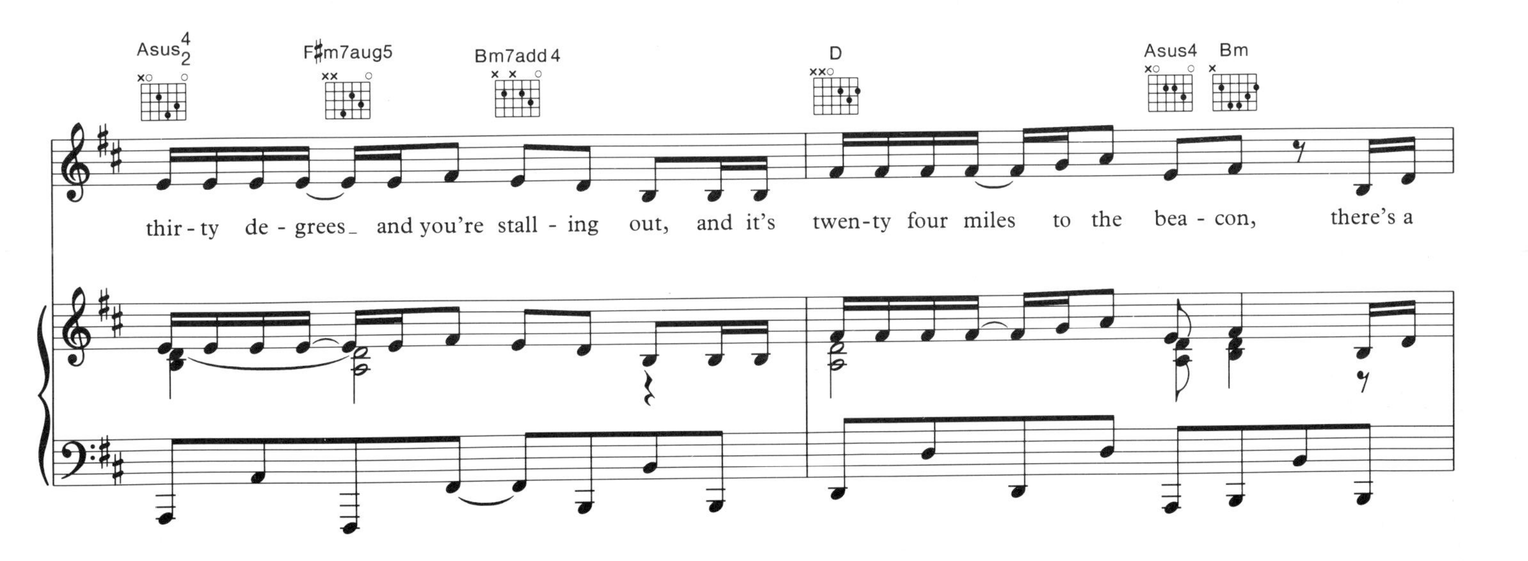

Asus4/2
F♯m7aug5
Bm7add4
Bm
E7no3
Bm
E7no3
A
Bm
E9no3
crack in the sky and the warn-ing's out.
Don't take that dive a-gain,
push
Bm
F♯m7aug5
D
Female voice
Asus4
A
through that band of rain.
Five miles out, just
hold your head-ing true. Got to get your
Bmadd4
Bm
D
E
F♯
D
Voices
fin - est out, you're num-ber one an-ti-ci-pat-ing you.
Climb - ing out, just
A
F♯m/A
Bm
D
E
F♯
hold your head-ing true. Got to get your
fin - est out, you're num-ber one an-ti-ci-pat-ing you.

B5
A5
Bagpipes
Bm
E
A
F♯m
D
F♯m/A
F♯
Electric guitar
Asus4
F♯m7
Vocoder
Traf-fic con-trol - ler is call - ing, Vic - tor,
Ju - liet your i - den - ti - ty, I have

30
D Asus4 Bm A F#m7 Bm E
lost in the vi - o-lent storm com-mu-ni - cate or squalk e - mer-gen-cy. Don't
Bm E A Bm E Bm F#m
Voices
take that dive a - gain, push through that band of rain. Lost in
Dm C Dm C Dm
sta - tic eight - een. And the storm is clos - ing in now. Au - to -
C Dm C Dm A5
Male voice
- ma - tic eight - een. (Got to push through.) Trapped in liv - ing hell. You're a

D5
G5
D5
G5
C5
3fr
pri - soner of the dark sky. The pro - pel-ler blades are still, the
D5
G5
D5
C5
3fr
A5
Female voice
e - vil eye of the hur-ri-cane is com-ing in now for the kill. Our
F
C
Dm
hope's with you, ri-der in the blue.
C
B♭
F
Gm
3fr
F
Gm
3fr
Wel - come's wait - ing. We're an - ti - ci - pat - ing you'll be

B♭
F
Gm
3fr
C
F
N.C.
F
ce - le-brat - ing when you're down and brak - ing.
Electric guitars
C
B♭/D
C/E
N.C.
Female voice
Climb - ing out.
Vocoder
Climb-ing, climb-ing.
F
C
Dm7
C5
3fr
Female voice
Five miles out.
Vocoder
Climb-ing, climb-ing.

F
C
Dm7
Voices
Five miles out. Just hold your head-ing true. Got to get your fin - est out.
C
Csus4
3fr
C
3fr
F
C
Vocoder
Climb-ing, climb-ing.
Voices
Five miles out. Just hold your head-ing true. Got to get your
B♭/D
C
Csus4
3fr
C
3fr
F
fin - est out.
Vocoder
Climb-ing, climb-ing.
Voices
Climb - ing out.
Five miles out.
Just
C
B♭/D
C/E
Csus4
3fr
C
3fr
Vocoder
repeat to fade
hold your head-ing true. Got to get your fin - est out.
Climb-ing, climb-ing.

to france

Words & Music by
Mike Oldfield

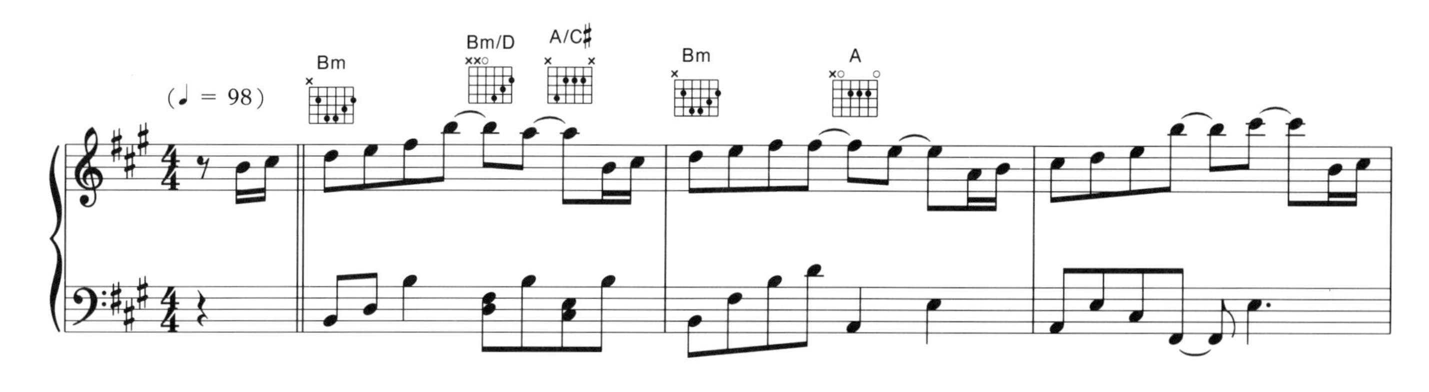

A F♯m Bm C♯m D E F♯m E E/G♯ F♯m
4fr 2fr 4fr 2fr 6fr
far from the is - lands. Don't you know you're ne - ver go - ing to
- ing for sanc - tu - a - ry. You know you're ne - ver go - ing to
D E F♯m F♯m E E/G♯ F♯m
2fr
get to France. Ma-ry Queen of chance will they find you? Ne - ver go-ing to
D E F♯m Bm
2fr
1.
get to France. Could a new ro - mance ev-er bind you?
D A Bm A Bm C♯m D E F♯m
4fr 2fr
2.
you?

Dadd9
D
A/C♯
D
E
I see a picture, by the lamps flicker.
Dadd9
D
A/C♯
D
E
Isn't it strange how dreams fade and shimmer?
F♯m
E
E/G♯
F♯m
D
E
F♯m
Never going to get to France. Mary Queen of chance will they find you?
F♯m
E
E/G♯
F♯m
D
E
F♯m
to Coda
Never going to get to France. Could a new romance ever bind you?

Bm
D
A
Bm
A
Bm
C♯m
4fr
D
E
2fr
D.𝄋 al Coda
E/B
F♯m
⊕ CODA
Ne - ver go-ing to
play 4 times ad lib.
Em/B
get to France.
Ne - ver go-ing to...

foreign affair

Words and Music by
Maggie Reilly and Mike Oldfield

G♯m7
wish - ful_ e - mo-tion, a drop in_ the o-cean, a hush in_ the air you can
B
C♯5
C♯sus4
C♯5
4fr
feel a - ny-where in the cool twi - light on a tro - pi - cal night.
F♯
B
F♯
B
F♯
C♯
F♯
C♯
Float - ing_ on_ air, for - eign af - fair. A ma - gi - cal po - tion.
F♯
C♯
A♯m
Cool lo - co - mo - tion, a dream, a
Ma - gi - cal po - tion, a cool lo - co - mo - tion.

D♯m
E♯m
3fr
D♯m
E♯m
3fr
F♯/A♯
G♯5
4fr
prayer, it's a for-eign af-fair.
C♯m
4fr
G♯m7
For - eign af - fair. Take a trip in the air to a tro - pi - cal beach, an
B
is - land to reach, a new ter - ri - to - ry for an in - ti - mate sto - ry, a la -
1–5.
6.
C♯5
4fr
C♯sus4
4fr
C♯5
4fr
C♯sus4
4fr
C♯5
4fr
N.C.
- goon par la mer. It's a for - eign af - fair. for - eign af - fair, for - eign.

in dulci jubilo

Arranged by
Mike Oldfield

C
F
C
F
C
Em
Recorder and kazoo
Am
Am/G
Dm
G
C
F
G
C
Am
Dm
G
C
F
G
C
F
C
G
C
C
F
C
F
C
Em
Recorder and penny whistle

Am
Am/G
Dm
G
C
F
G
C
Am
Dm
G
C
F
G
C
F
C
G
C
C
F
C
F
C
Em
Recorder, penny whistle and kazoo
Am
Am/G
Dm
G
C
F
G
C
Am

Dm
G
C
F
G
C
F
C
G
C
Recorder and penny whistle
Em
Am
Am/G
Electric guitar

C
F
C
F
C
Em
Am
Am/G
Dm
G
C
F
G
C
Am
Dm
G
C
F
G
C
F
C
G
C
C
F
C
F
C
Em

Am
Am/G
Dm
G
C
F
G
C
Am
Dm
G
C
F
G
C
F
C
G
C
C
F
C
F
C
Em
Am
Am/G
Dm
G
C
F
G
C
Am

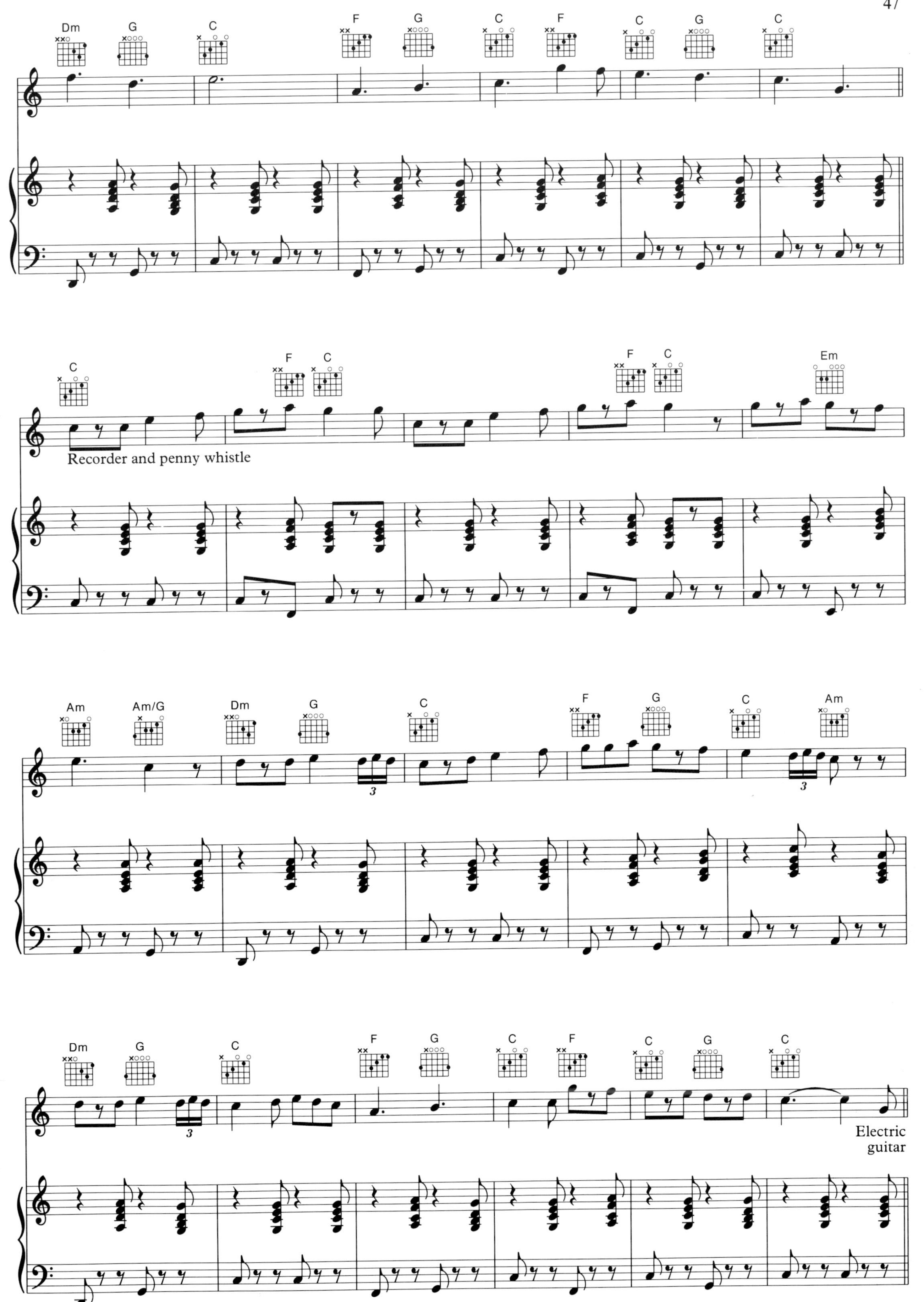
Dm
G
C
F
G
C
F
C
G
C
C
F
C
F
C
Em
Recorder and penny whistle
Am
Am/G
Dm
G
C
F
G
C
Am
Dm
G
C
F
G
C
F
C
G
C
Electric guitar

48
C
F
C
F
C
Em
Am
Am/G
Dm
G
C
add recorder and penny whistle
F
G
C
Am
Dm
G
C
rit.
F
G
C
F
C
G
C

shadow on the wall

Words & Music by
Mike Oldfield

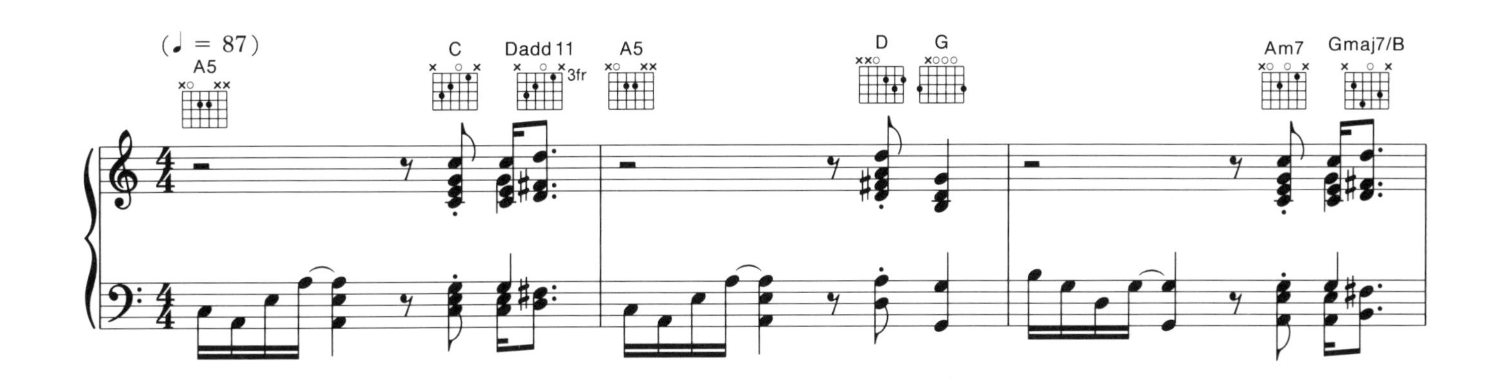

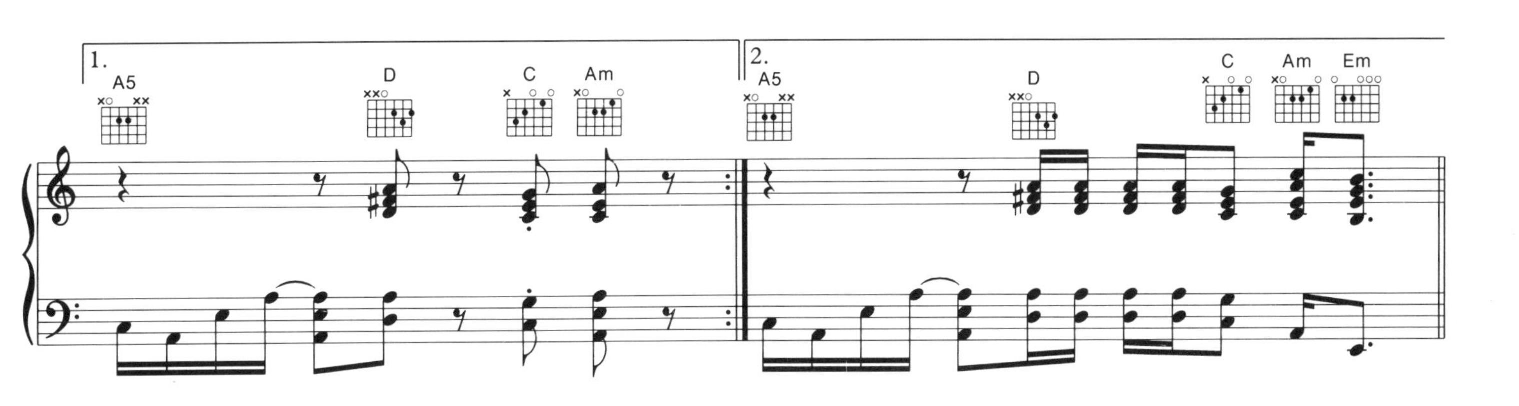

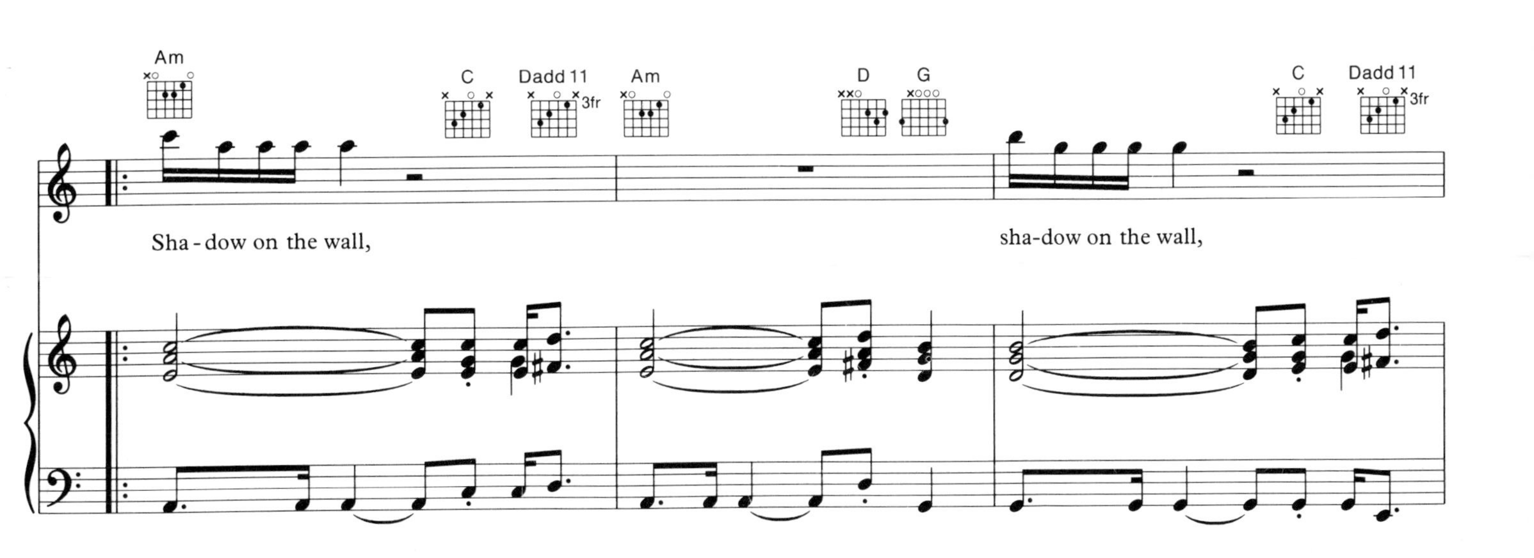

1.
2.
Am
Am
black shadow on the wall.
A5
2fr
G5
Esus4
Em
1. Treat me like a pri-son-er, treat me like a fool, treat me like a los-er,
2. Treat me like I'm ev-il, freeze me till I'm cold, beat me till I'm fee-ble,
Am
G
D/F♯
Am/E
A5
2fr
G5
use me as a tool. Waste me till I'm hun-gry, loose me in the cold,
grind me till I'm old. Wire me till I'm tir-ed, push me till I fall,
Esus4
Em/G
D
C
Am
Em
treat me like a cri-mi-nal, just a sha-dow on the wall.

Am
C
Dadd 11
3fr
Am
D
G
C
Dadd 11
3fr
Sha-dow on the wall,
sha-dow on the wall,
Am
Am
C
Dadd 11
3fr
Am
D
G
sha-dow on the wall,
C
Dadd 11
3fr
1.
Am
2.
Am
Electric guitar
sha-dow on the wall,
black sha-dow on the wall.
black sha-dow on the wall.
G
3
Electric guitars

Em
Am
Em
Banjo
Am
C
Dadd 11
3fr
Am
D
G
C
Dadd 11
3fr
Sha-dow on the wall,
sha-dow on the wall,
1.
Am
2.
Am
black sha-dow on the wall.
black sha-dow on the wall.
Am7
G/B
Am
D
G
Am7
G/B
Sha-dow on the wall,
sha-dow on the wall,

Am
Am
D
G
black sha-dow on the wall.
Night, blue sha - dow,
1.
Am
D5
C5
3fr
A5
2.
Am
D5
C5
3fr
A5
treat me like a sha - dow.
sha - dow.
Synth
Am
D
G
add Electric guitar
Am
D5
C5
3fr
A5
Am

D
G
Am
D5
C5
A5
3fr
Am
D
G
Sha - dow on the wall. Night, blue sha - dow, treat me like a
1.2.
Am
D5
C5
A5
3fr
sha - dow.
3.
Am
D5
C5
B5
A5
3fr
sha - dow.
Electric guitar
A5
2fr
G

Em7
A5
E5
Am
C
G5/D
add 2nd Electric guitar
Electric guitar
Sha-dow on the wall. Night, blue
Am
D
G
C
G5
Am
sha - dow._
Sha-dow on the wall. Treat me like a sha - dow._
Black sha-dow on the wall.
Am
Asus4/2
Am
G
Em/G
A5
2fr
Sha-dow on the wall. Black sha - dow,_ treat me like a sha - dow._
Am
Asus4/2
Am
G
Em/G
A5
2fr
repeat to fade
Night, blue sha - dow,_ treat me like a sha - dow._
Black sha-dow on the wall.

islands

Words & Music by
Mike Oldfield

D
Bm
G
1. Is - lands, from the first time we saw, we could wait for this mo - ment like
2. Is - lands nev - er been to be - fore, and we climb so high, to where the
D/A
D
Bm
rocks on the shore. We can nev - er be clo - ser some - how, for the
wild birds soar. There's a new path that we found just to - day, I was
G
D/A
D
G/D
A/D
mo - ment that lasts is this mo - ment now. When the
lost in the for - est and you showed me the way.
D
G
A
D
night's on fire oh will you keep the can - dle - light burn - ing, hold

Gmaj9 G A D Gmaj9 G
on to your hearts de-si - re. When you see one bird__ in-to the wind
A A/D D Bm G A
__ a-no-ther one's turn - ing, and the two can__ fly__ much high - er.__ We are
D Em A
is - lands but nev-er too far,__ we are is - lands, and I need your light to-night and I
D
need your light__ to-night. We are is - lands but nev-er too far,__ we are

Two Electric guitars
Water drop sound
Electric guitar and vocals

Vocals
Electric guitar

3

Am7
12fr
Em7
7fr
Vocals
doubled with flute sound and Acoustic guitar
Dm7
5fr
Am
5fr
Am7
12fr
Em7
7fr
Dm7
5fr
Am
5fr
N.C.

Am
5fr
Electric guitar
Vocals
Electric guitar

Classical guitar
Keyboard
8vb
Em7
7fr
Classical guitar
pizzicato string sound
Cmaj7
3fr
Bm
2fr
F♯sus2
Cm7sus4
4fr
A♭add 9
4fr
Gm/B♭
Asus4

Am
5fr
Vocals
fade
Electric guitar
Vocals
Electric guitar

ommadawn

Music by
Mike Oldfield

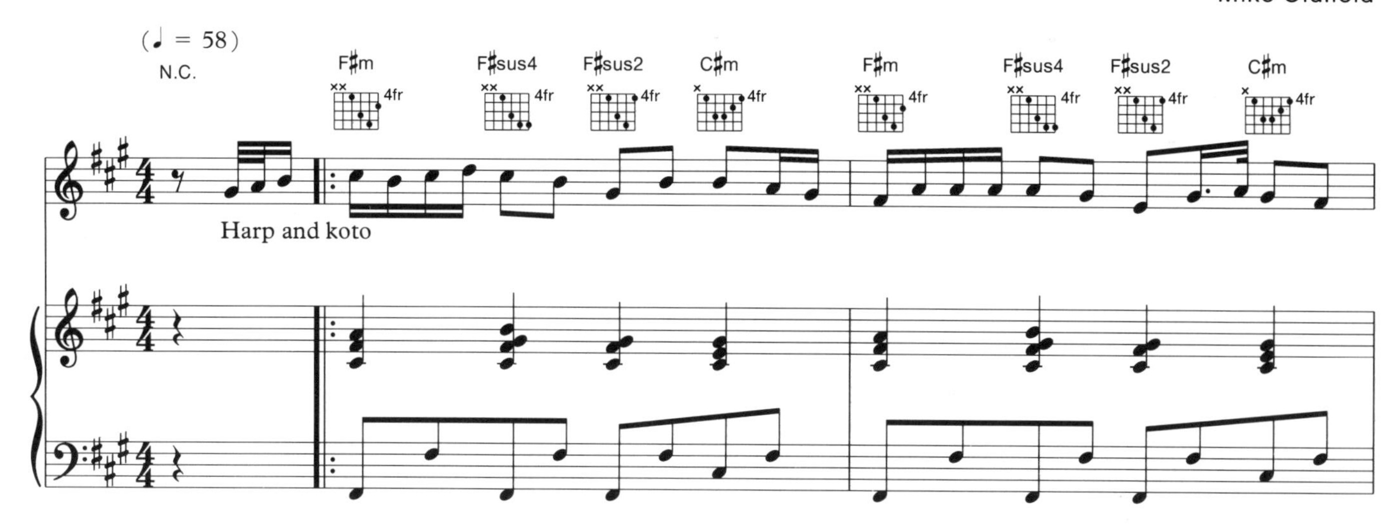

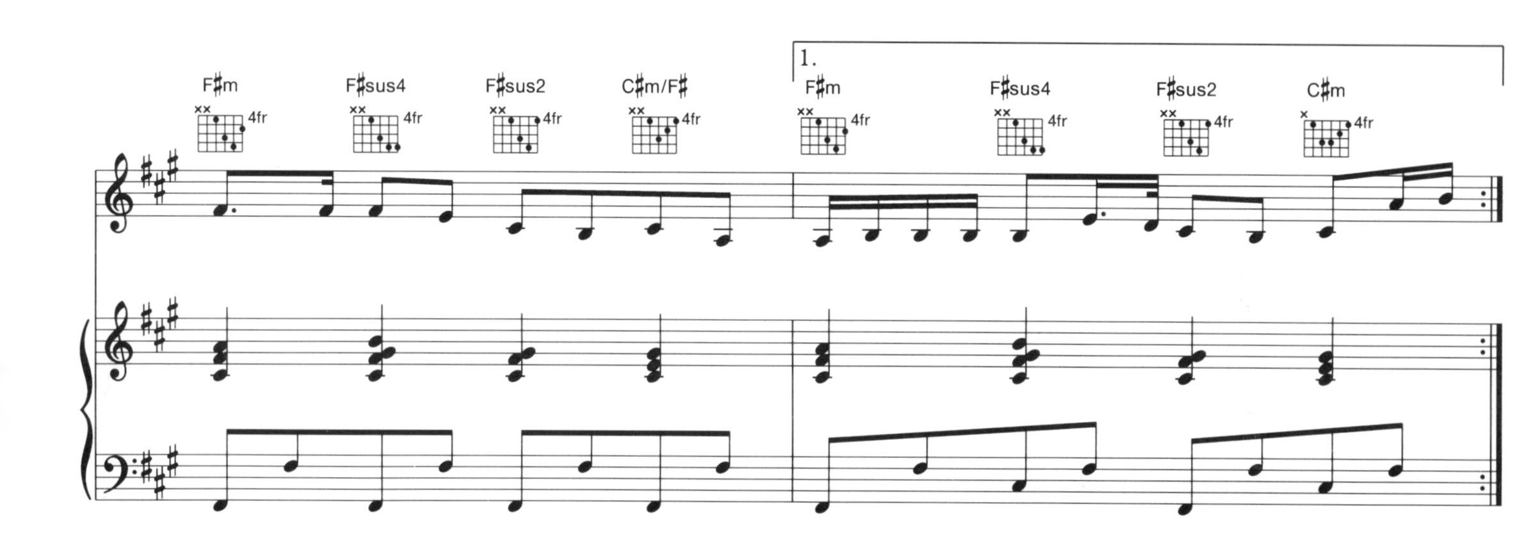

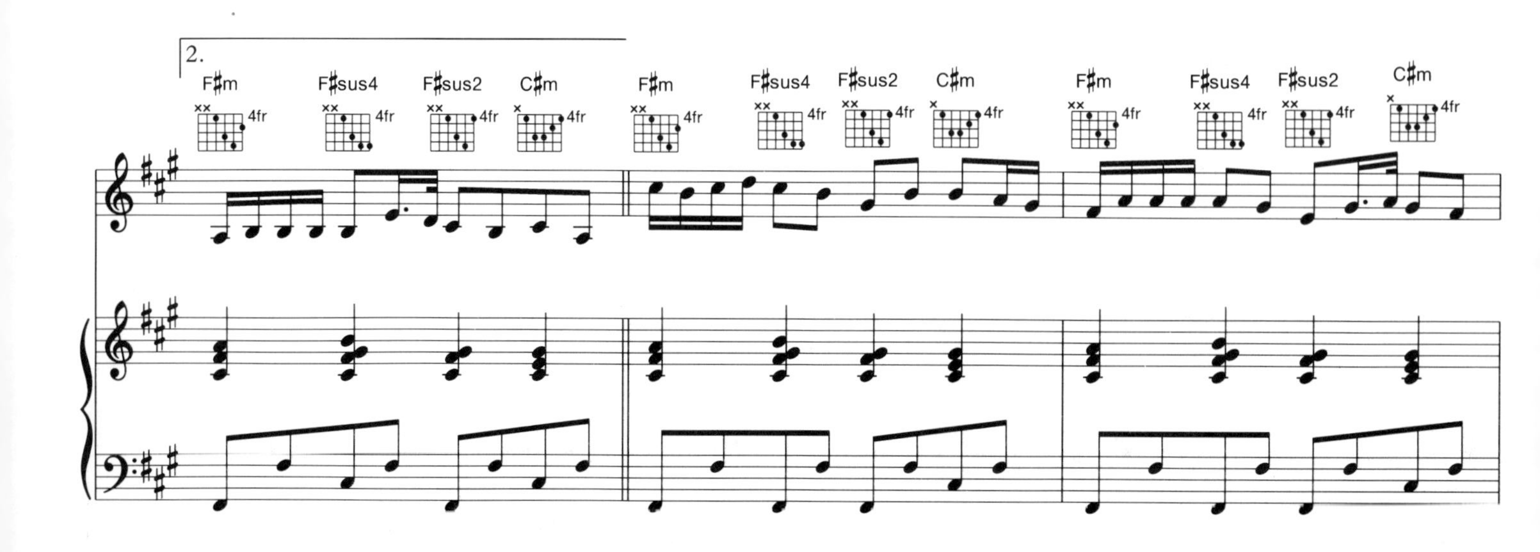

F♯m
F♯sus4
F♯sus2
C♯m/F♯
F♯m
F♯sus4
F♯sus2
C♯m
F♯m
F♯sus4
F♯sus2
C♯m
4fr
F♯m
F♯sus4
F♯sus2
C♯m
F♯m
F♯sus4
F♯sus2
C♯m/F♯
F♯m
F♯sus4
F♯sus2
C♯m
F♯5
8va
N.C.
(8va)

Classical guitar
(8va)
F♯m
F♯sus4
F♯sus2
C♯m
C♯m/F♯
4fr

F♯m
F♯sus4
F♯sus2
C♯m
F♯m
F♯sus4
F♯sus2
C♯m
F♯m
F♯sus4
F♯sus2
C♯m
F♯m
F♯sus4
F♯sus2
C♯m/F♯
F♯m
F♯sus4
F♯sus2
C♯m
F♯5
8va
N.C.
(8va)

(8va)
Electric guitar
(8va)
fade
(8va)
(8va)

portsmouth

Arranged by
Mike Oldfield

G
C
F
1.
C
G
C
2.
C
G
C
G
C
F
C
G
C
F
C
G
1.
C
2.
C
G
C
F
1.
C
G
C
G
2.
C
G
C

incantations – part four

Music by
Robert Howes, Barbara Courtney-King,
Steve Davies and William McGillivray

F♯m
G
Em
F♯m
G
A
Bm
A
Synth strings
F♯m
G
Em
F♯m
G
A
Bm
A

F♯m
G
Em
A
D
Electric guitar
Bm
C
Am
Female vocal
1. Queen and hunt - ress chaste and fair,_ now the
(2.) not an en - vious shade, dare it -
(3.) bow of pearl a - part, and the
(4.) us en - treats thy light, god - dess

Bm
C
Am
sun is laid to sleep, seat - ed in a sil - ver chair, state in
- self to in - ter - pose, Cyn - thia's shin - ing orb was made, heav'n to
cry - stal shin - ing quiver, give un - to the fly - ing hart, space to
ex - cel-lent - ly bright, bless us then with wish - ed sight, thou who
1.2.3.
4.
(♩ = 83)
Bm
C
D
C
D
Em
wont - ed man-ner keep. 2. Earth let night.
cheer when day did close. 3. Lay the
breathe how short so ever. 4. Hes - per -
makes a day of
Electric guitar
D
Bm
C
poco rit.
Am
Bm
C
D
E7sus4
2fr

amarok

Words & Music by
Mike Oldfield

D♯m/F♯
C♯/F♯
4fr
B/F♯
four times
So far so far so far so far so far so far so.
D♯m7
C♯
4fr
B
So far so far so far so far so far so far so.
N.C.
C♯
4fr
B
So far so far so far so far so far so far so.
N.C.
C♯
4fr
B
Synth
D
So far so far so far so far so far so far so.

E
F♯
F♯5
Telephone
N.C.
What?
D/F♯
Dadd♯11/F♯
E6add9
E
F♯
N.C.
What?
D/F♯
N.C.
E/F♯
N.C.

1.
2.
F♯m7
Emaj7
4fr
5fr
Far so far so so far so so far so so far so. so so far so.
N.C.
three times
so so far so. Far so far far so far far so far far so far.
Female vocal

Printed in England
Panda Press · Haverhill · Suffolk • 3/94